SCHOLASTIC

Let's Find Out

My REBUS Reader

I0890037

On My Way to School

by Amanda Miller

SCHOLASTIC INC.

New York Toronto London Auckland Sydney New Delhi Hong Kong

I see my neighbors on my way to  .

school

I see a shopkeeper on my way to  .

school

I see a dog walker on my way to 

.

school

I see a mail carrier on my way to  .

school

I see a police officer on my way to 

school

I am at  . I see my teacher. Hello, friends!

school

BIG WORD community

A **community** is a group of people who work and play together
Have you seen these workers in your community?

police officer

firefighter

veterinarian

chef

mail carrier

doctor

mechanic